To Louise, teacher extraordinaire
—L.J.H.

To Ted the Pilot; and with many
thanks to the Hurricane Watchers
of Turtle Trail: Barb, Daniel and
Tasha, Henry and Deb
—J.W.

Text copyright © 1995 by Lorraine Hopping Egan.
Illustrations copyright © 1995 by Jody Wheeler.
All rights reserved. Published by Scholastic Inc.
Printed in the U.S.A.
ISBN 0-590-06683-8
HELLO READER!, CARTWHEEL BOOKS, and the CARTWHEEL BOOKS logo are registered trademarks of Scholastic Inc.

5 6 7 8 9   23   03 02 01 00 99 98